G Wardlow

EITB
Engineering Industry
Training Board

Basic Engineering
Training Guide

Milling

ISBN 0 85083 705 7

Introduction

This guide is one of a series prepared to assist instructors and trainees in the development of engineering skills and knowledge. The various areas of skill to which each guide refers are illustrated with drawings supported by notes on methods and procedures.

There are often a number of ways of carrying out a particular operation or activity and no attempt has been made to include alternatives. It is not intended that the methods illustrated are the ones which must be taught but instructors who choose to teach other methods must ensure that they are safe and efficient.

Trainees should be issued with guides relevant to the skill area in which they are being trained.

The guides are useful as:
- A self-teaching aid for trainees following demonstration of a particular skill element by an instructor.
- A reminder for instructors of correct procedures and of the key points to be emphasised.

To help instructors and trainees to cross refer the content of these guides to the Basic Engineering Training Specifications the Instructional Objective index numbers given in the specifications are shown in brackets after the relevant subject headings within the guides.

No attempt has been made to cover the related workshop theory which is an essential feature of complementary courses of further education. However, elements of job knowledge are included where they need to be given additional emphasis or are required to complement the skill training before the theory has been covered in the college course.

! *SAFETY – Attention is drawn to safety aspects throughout the guides. Instructors and trainees are requested to pay particular attention to this subject at all times.*

The following symbols are used within the illustrations to depict particular attention points such as sound, vision and movement.

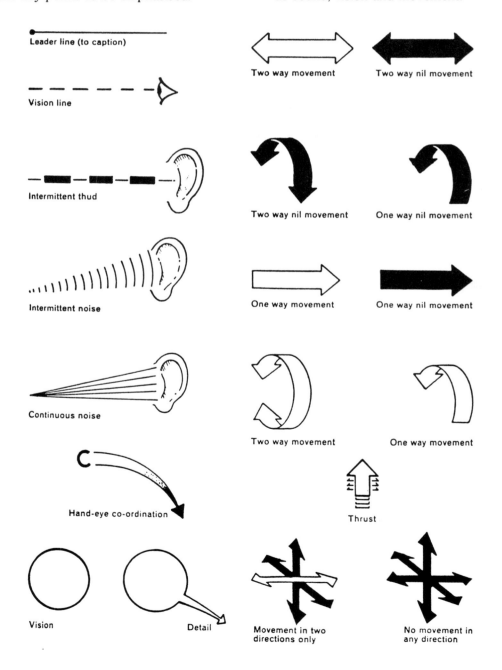

Contents

Introduction and standard symbols

Safety rules   1

Types of milling machine   2
Horizontal milling machine   2
Universal milling machine   3
Vertical milling machine   4

Cutters (M2)   5
Face mill   5
End mill   5
Slot drills   5
Roller or slab mill   5
Side and face cutters   5
Interlocking cutters   6
Slitting saws   6
Slotting cutters   7
Angle cutters   7
T-slot cutters   7
Form relieved cutters   8
Convex cutters   8

Mounting cutters (M2)   9
Mounting cutters direct to machine spindle -
vertical machine   9
Engaging cutters on stub arbor   10
Engaging taper shank cutters in machine
spindle   10
Engaging straight shank cutters in automatic
chucks   11
Disengaging cutters from automatic centring
chucks   11
Mounting cutters in collett chuck   12
Engaging arbor mounted cutters - vertical
machine   12
Engaging arbor mounted cutters - horizontal
machine   13

Cutting speeds, feeds and coolants (M3 – M4)   16
Cutting speed   16
Cutter feed   16
Feed   16
Cutting fluids   16

Workholding (M5 – M6)   18
Setting vice parallel with tenons   18
Setting vice parallel without tenons   18
Clamping regular shaped workpiece in vice   19
Setting to datum face   19
Setting work to marking out   20

Milling operations (M7 – M11)   21
Milling a block square   21
Facing to length on a vertical machine   21
Facing to length on a horizontal machine   23
Milling a shoulder   23
Milling tenons   24
Milling a slot   26
Milling a keyway   27
Milling vees on a horizontal machine   27
Milling an angle by setting the work at an
angle   27

Safety rules

The following safety rules apply particularly to the operation and maintenance of machine tools such as lathes, milling machines and shaping machines. Ask your instructor immediately if you are in the slightest doubt about your machine.

Personal safety

Do:
- Immediately report any accidents, however small.
- Wear safety glasses.
- Wear safety footwear.
- Use the protective cream provided.
- Wear your overalls buttoned up to protect your clothing and prevent loose clothing and ties becoming caught in moving parts of machines.
- Either roll up your overall sleeves or button up the cuffs.
- Keep your hair short or wear a cap, net or headband.

Do not:
- Wear rings or watches while operating a machine.
- Keep sharp tools in your overall pockets.
- Remove swarf with bare hands; use a brush.
- Manually lift heavy equipment.
- Lean on the machine.

Machine safety

Do:
- Keep machines and all equipment clean, and in good condition.
- Before starting a machine ensure that you know how to stop it.
- Switch off the machine immediately anything goes wrong.
- Keep the machine and surrounding area tidy.
- Check oil levels before first starting machines.
- Switch off machine at mains at end of each day.
- Check that chucks or cutters rotate in the correct direction before commencing cutting operations.
- Use the correct tool or cutter for the job.
- Replace tools that are worn or damaged.
- Keep tools and cutters in boxes or racks when not in use.
- Report immediately to your instructor any mechanical or electrical fault.
- Ensure that all machine guards are in position before starting the machine.
- Check that the work area is clear before starting the machine.
- Ensure that everything is properly secured before starting the machine.
- Ensure that feed mechanisms are not engaged before starting the machine.

Do not:
- Attempt to operate a machine until you know how to use it correctly.
- Tamper with a machine.
- Remove any stops in an effort to obtain a greater cutting range, or the machine may be seriously damaged.
- Try and reverse the direction of a spindle while it is in motion.
- Try to change a spindle speed while it is in motion.
- Throw things.
- Walk away and leave your machine running.
- Direct compressed air at yourself or workmates. It can kill.
- Leave crane hook over machine, or the surrounding area after use.

Types of milling machine (M1)

Horizontal milling machine

The table of the horizontal milling machine moves horizontally both parallel and at right angles to the axis of spindle. This type of machine is used for machining horizontal and vertical faces and slots.

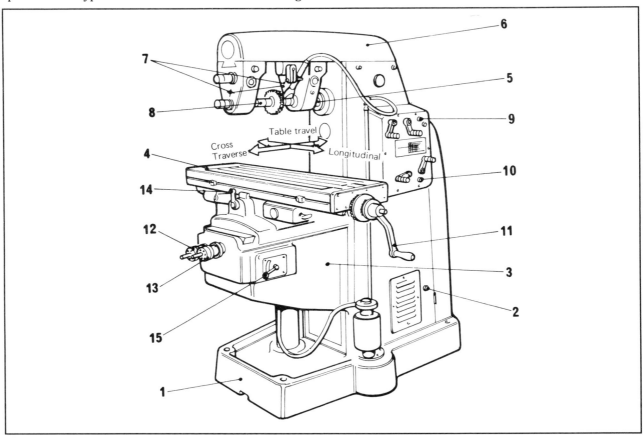

Identification of main parts

Code	Name	Location	Function
1	Base	Main body	Forms part of column Storage tank for coolant
2	Column	Rear of main body	Houses drive motor
3	Knee	Front of column	Carries machine table Houses various machine controls
4	Table	Top of knee	Carries suitably mounted workpiece to the cutter
5	Spindle	Horizontally mounted at top of column	Provides mounting point and drive for arbor
6	Overarm	Horizontally mounted at top of column	Carries arbor support brackets
7	Arbor support brackets (steadies)	Mounted underneath overarm	Supports outer end of arbor
8	Arbor	Mounted on spindle nose	Provides extension to spindle for mounting cutter

9	Spindle speed gearbox	Top right hand side of column	Selects speed of rotation of spindle
10	Table feed gearbox	Right hand side of column	Provides selection of automatic feeds for table
11	Table hand feed (longitudinal)	Both ends of table (detachable handle)	Moves table towards or away from cutter
12	Table vertical travel control	Left hand front of knee (detachable handle)	Raises or lowers table
13	Table cross travel control	Right hand front of knee (detachable handle)	Moves table towards or away from column
14	Table traverse	Middle front of table	Selects direction of table traverse
15	Start and stop lever	Right hand side of knee	Switches electricity supply to machine on or off.

Universal milling machine

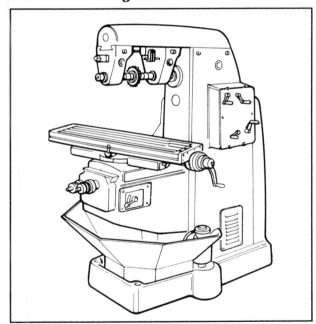

A universal milling machine has a swivelling table thus making it capable of more complex forms of machining such as the cutting of all types of helical grooves and slots, spur and spiral gears and the spiral fluting of drills.

The main parts are as shown for the horizontal milling machine.

Vertical milling machine

The vertical milling machine has the spindle mounted vertically at right angles to the table. Most work on this type of machine is done by using end and face milling cutters.

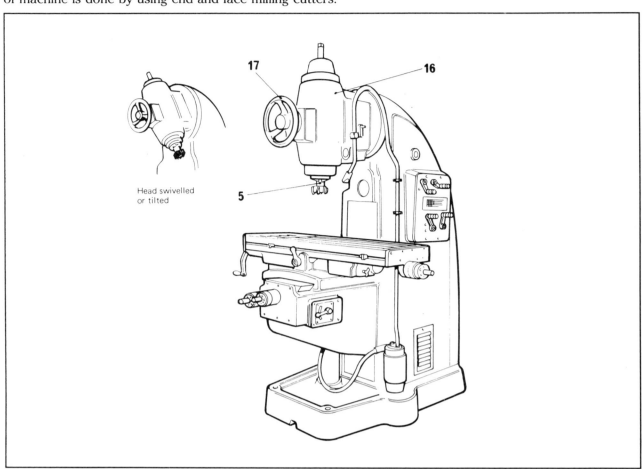

Head swivelled
or tilted

Identification of main parts

Code	Name	Location	Function
1,2, 3 & 4	As stated for horizontal milling machine	Main body & column	
5	Spindle	Vertically mounted in head	Provides mounting and drive for cutter
9, 10, 11, 12, 13, 14 & 15	As stated for horizontal milling machine	Column, knee and table	
16	Vertical head	Mounted on top front of column	Houses spindle
17	Spindle vertical adjustment handle	Front of vertical head	Provides vertical traverse for spindle

Cutters (M2)

Face mill

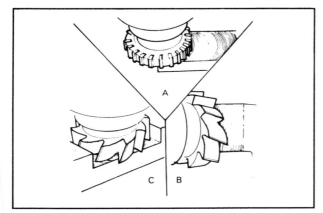

Face mills are used to produce flat surfaces as illustrated above.
- Facing the top of a workpiece on a vertical mill (A).
- Facing the end or edge of a workpiece on a horizontal mill (B).
- Milling shallow steps in workpiece (C).

Cutter selection
- The most convenient largest diameter cutter to cover the face to be machined should be selected if the face is approximately central to cutter.
- The smallest diameter cutter to cover the face to be machined should be selected if machining to a shoulder.
- The number of teeth in the cutter to be used is determined by the material and the rigidity of the workpiece. Coarse tooth cutters are desirable as they are more efficient, but thin parts require finer tooth cutters to avoid workpiece distortion.
- The grade of cutter teeth to use is determined by the material and possibly by the number of workpieces to be produced. Tipped cutters are best for cast iron and other ferrous metals.

End mill

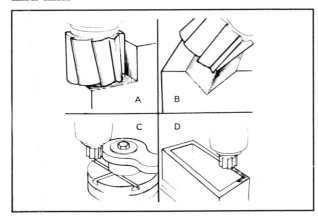

Typical applications are illustrated as follows:
- Milling a shoulder (A).
- Milling angular faces (B).
- Milling internal and external profiles (C).
- Milling flat edges or faces (D).

Cutter selection
- Select smallest diameter cutter to cover face when milling to a shoulder.
- Select the most convenient largest diameter cutter to machine a flat face with the cutter face.
- The number of teeth in the cutter to be used is determined by the material and the rigidity of the workpiece. Coarse tooth cutters with a quick spiral are generally more efficient, but thin parts require finer teeth to avoid distortion.

Slot drills
Typical applications are illustrated below:

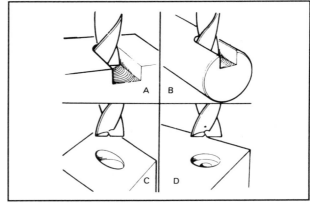

- Milling slots (A).
- Milling keyways (B).
- Milling a flat seat on angular or curved surface (C).
- Milling small counterbores or spot facing (D).

Cutter selection
- Size of cutter is determined by the width of the slot, or the diameter of the hole to be cut.
Note: If the slot is not a standard width, the largest standard size cutter below the width of the slot is used and equal amounts then removed from each side wall of slot.
- The choice of straight or helical teeth is determined by the material and rigidity of the workpiece. Helical teeth are desirable for heavy cuts but thin walled workpieces or shallow slots are best cut with a straight toothed cutter.

Roller or slab mill
Typical applications are:

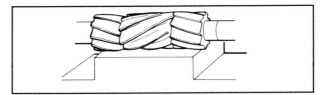

Milling the top face of a workpiece.

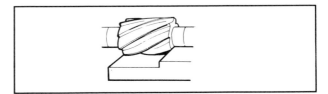

Milling to a shoulder.

Cutter selection
- Select the most convenient smallest diameter cutter.
- Select a pair of interlocking cutters of exactly the same diameter and with opposite spiral angles if a wide face is to be machined.

Side and face cutters

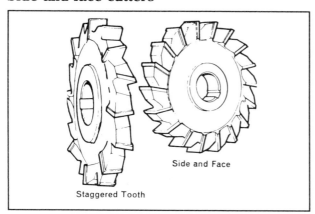

Side and Face

Staggered Tooth

Side and face cutters are disc-like cutters with teeth which cut on each side as well as on the periphery. Sometimes a cutter is made to cut on one side only; this type is called a half side milling cutter. Another type has alternate teeth on each side of the cutter; this is a staggered tooth cutter.

Cutter selection
- Select the most convenient smallest diameter cutter.
- Select a normal type cutter if only light cuts are required.
- Select coarse staggered tooth cutters to take heavy cuts.

Interlocking cutters

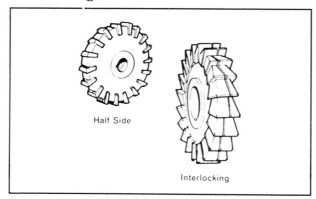

Half Side

Interlocking

Interlocking cutters are made so that two cutters may be placed side by side with the teeth interlocked. Slots may be cut with these cutters, the width being adjusted by placing shims between the cutter bosses.
Side and face mills are often used in pairs to mill parallel side faces and are frequently referred to as straddle mills.

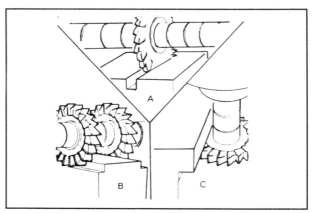

A

B   C

Typical applications are:
- Milling a vertical face.
- Milling a step.
- Milling a slot (see A above).
- Milling 90° vees.
- In pairs, milling parallel faces. This is known as straddle milling (see B above).
- Back facing on vertical mill (see C above).

Slitting saws
Typical applications are illustrated below:

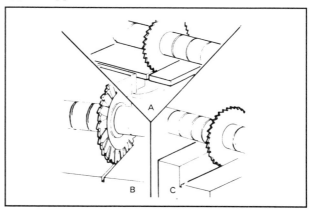

A

B   C

- Cutting off material to length (A).
- Milling narrow slots (B).
- Undercutting corners (C).

Cutter selection
- Select smallest diameter cutter possible.
- Select a saw with side teeth for cutting deep and wide slots.
- Check that teeth corners are not worn or chipped.

! *SAFETY — Slitting saws must not be keyed to the spindle.*

Slotting cutters

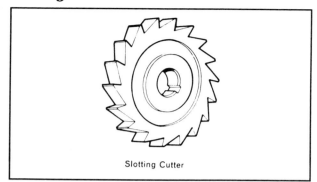

Slotting Cutter

Slotting cutters are narrow cylindrical cutters very similar to the side and face type, but with teeth on the periphery only. The teeth are usually straight on cutters up to 20 mm wide while wider cutters have spiral teeth.

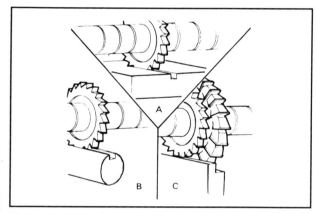

Typical applications are illustrated above:
• Milling slots (A).
• Milling keyways (B).
• Milling narrow flat faces (C).

Cutter selection
Select cutter of correct width when cutting a slot.

Angle cutters

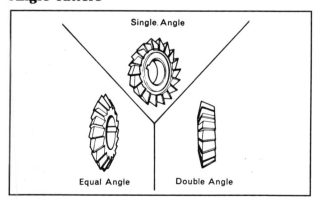

Single Angle

Equal Angle   Double Angle

Angle cutters are similar to small side and face cutters except that one or more sides of the teeth are ground at an angle to the axis.

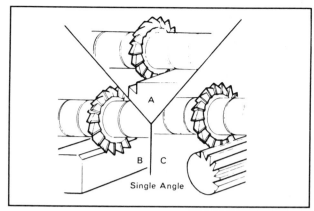

Single Angle

Typical applications are:

Single angle cutters
• Milling an angle on the side of workpiece.
• Milling dovetails (see A above).
• Chamfering the corners of a workpiece (see B above).
• Milling straight flutes with radial face (see C above).

Equal angle cutters
• Milling vee grooves in a workpiece.

Double angle cutters
• Milling spiral flutes with radial face.

T-slot cutters

T-slot cutters are made with taper or parallel shanks exactly the same as those of end mills and are held in the same way. The teeth are similar to a plain milling cutter but cut on each side as well as on the periphery. They are often staggered to give a better cutting action and more chip clearance.

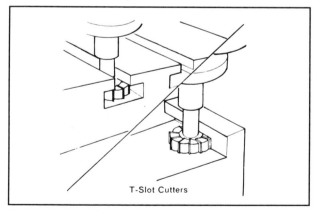

T-Slot Cutters

T-slots are cut in two operations. The primary slot is made with an end mill or slotting cutter. The wider part is then cut with a T-slot cutter.
T-slot cutters are used almost exclusively to cut T-slots, but they may also be used to cut slots which are inaccessible to other slotting cutters.

Form relieved cutters

Form relieved cutters are made in many shapes and sizes and play an important part in milling. They are used to duplicate accurately a profile of special shape and should only be used for the purpose for which they are designed.

Convex cutters

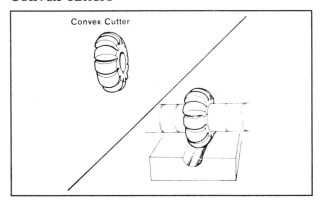

These are used to form an internal radius or groove upon workpiece.

Mounting cutters (M2)

Mounting cutters direct to machine spindle - vertical machine

! *SAFETY – Ensure machine is electrically isolated before commencing any cutter mounting operation.*

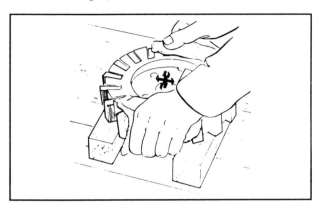

To position cutter on table:
- Place two blocks of wood on the table, on which to rest the cutter.

Note: Ensure maximum amount possible of cutter face will rest on blocks, but with sufficient space between the blocks to enable hand to engage securing screws through cutter body into spindle nose.
- Lift cutter, and place teeth down on top of blocks.
- Clean face of spindle nose and counterbore of cutter.

! *SAFETY – Protect hands with wiper when lifting cutter.*

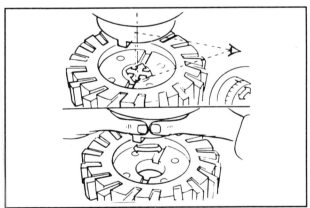

To centralise machine spindle:
- Raise machine table until top face of cutter is approximately 75 to 100 mm below spindle nose.
- Adjust table position to position diameter of spindle nose central to counterbore of cutter.
- Disengage drive to allow spindle to be rotated by hand. Align the spindle drive dogs with slots at the bottom of the counterbore of the cutter.

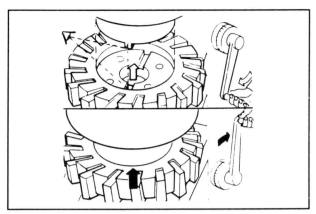

To engage cutter to spindle:
- Hand wind the table up, visually checking the spindle nose is central to cutter counterbore.
- Hand wind table up slowly until solid resistance to turn of hand crank is just felt.

Note: Do not forcibly turn hand crank when resistance is felt, or the lead screw will be damaged.

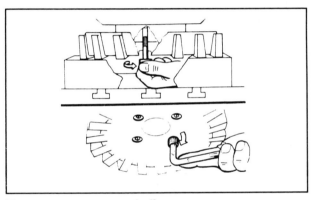

To secure cutter to spindle nose:
- Position securing screw, (usually a socket head set screw) through cutter body, and finger tighten ensuring head fully enters counterbore.

Note: If the threaded hole in spindle nose is not correctly aligned to hole in cutter body, the drive dogs are not correctly engaged in drive slot. Lower the table and realign them.
- Position the other securing screws and finger tighten.
- Lower machine table and remove blocks.
- Tighten screws securely using correct size key.

Note: When disengaging the cutter from the machine spindle the reverse procedure is adopted.

Engaging cutters on stub arbor

Engage arbor in machine spindle.
Prepare arbor as follows:
- Hold bushes in position and remove securing nut.
- Remove collars and key from arbor.
- Clean collars and arbor faces.

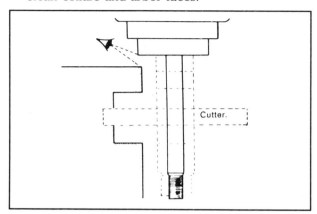

To decide cutter position on arbor:
- Refer to drawings and workpiece, to decide the best position of the cutter to obtain the maximum possible rigidity but ensuring the arbor and workpiece will be clear of any obstruction.

Note: The closer the cutter is positioned to the nose of the spindle the greater the rigidity obtained.
- Decide the number and width of collars to position the cutter in the correct position on arbor.

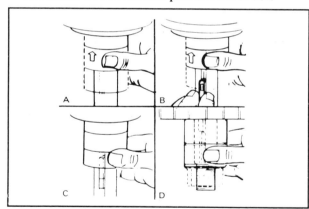

To engage cutter on arbor:
- Slide collar/collars up to shoulder of arbor one less than number required to position cutter (see A above).
- Fit key in arbor keyway, ensuring that key will protrude into collars at each side of cutter (see B above).
- Align keyway in collar to key in arbor and slide collar on arbor (see C above).
- Align keyway of cutter to key and slide cutter up to collars ensuring cutting edge is facing in the required direction (see D above).

Note: Thin cutters should be held between two collars for easier sliding onto arbor.
- Align keyway and slide collar(s) on arbor.
- Visually check that collar just protrudes onto threaded part of arbor, but leaving sufficient thread to engage nut fully.

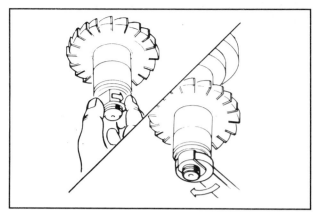

To tighten cutter on arbor:
- Hold bottom collar up to keep cutter in position.
- Engage nut on thread and finger tighten. Moderately tighten nut with spanner.

Engaging taper shank cutters in machine spindle

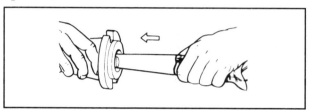

Select arbor as follows:
- Use the shortest arbor possible.
- Internal taper the same size as cutter taper.
- If necessary to use taper sleeves keep number used to minimum.

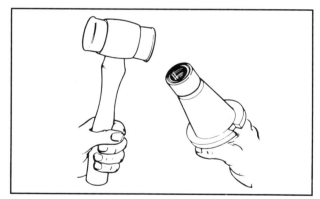

To engage cutter in arbor:
- Clean taper in arbor and cutter shank and remove any burrs.
- Align cutter tang to slot in taper, and engage tapers with a sharp thrust.
- Tap cutter in with soft hammer.

! *SAFETY – Care of hands on sharp edges of cutters.*

Engage arbor in machine spindle as follows:
• Clean both tapers.
• Engage drive dogs in arbor slots.
• Hold cutter in position applying upward pressure.
• Screw drawbar firmly into arbor.
• Switch on machine.
• Rotate spindle at a moderate speed, to visually check cutter runs true.

Note: When using morse taper cutters with a tapped shank, an open-ended adaptor should be used to allow the drawbar to screw direct into the cutter tang.

When removing this type of cutter from the arbor, screw a bolt of the same thread size into the tapped end of the shank and tap head of the bolt with a copper hammer to shock cutter free.

Engaging straight shank cutters in automatic locking chucks

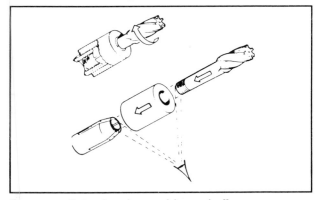

Engage collet arbor in machine spindle.
To engage cutter in collet:
• Select collet the same size as cutter shank.
• Insert chamfered end of collet into sleeve and slide collet in.
• Slip cutter into collet and screw in to just engage threads.

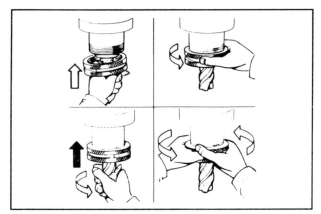

To engage cutter in arbor:
• Push sleeve and collet into arbor.
• Rotate collet and feel drive dogs engage in holes at bottom of arbor bore.
• Screw nut on arbor until a slight resistance is met.
• Screw in cutter until solid resistance is felt, to engage arbor centre in centre hole of cutter.
• Hand tighten cutter as tight as possible.
• Hand tighten nut as tight as possible or lightly tighten with special spanner supplied.

! *SAFETY – Protect hands with wiper when screwing cutter into collet.*

Note: Cleanliness is essential. Ensure all parts of chuck are thoroughly clean before assembly.

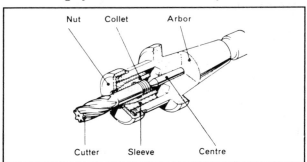

The completed assembly is illustrated above.

Disengaging cutters from automatic centring chucks

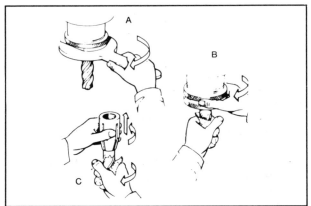

To disengage cutter:
• Engage low gear on machine spindle.

- Loosen locking nut with special spanner provided and remove nut from arbor (see A previous page).
- Pull cutter out to remove sleeve and collet from arbor (see B previous page).

! *SAFETY — Protect hands by wrapping wiper round cutter flutes.*

- Unscrew cutter and slide from collet (see C previous page).
- Clean all parts of chuck before storing away.

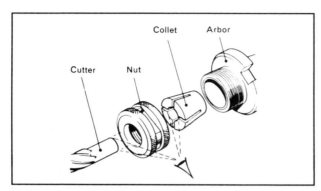

If changing cutter for one with same size shank:
- Loosen locking nut approximately half a turn.
- Unscrew cutter and slide from collet.
- Engage new cutter in collet and screw up to centre.
- Hand tighten locking nut.

Mounting cutters in collet chuck

Engage collet arbor in machine spindle.
To engage collet in arbor:
- Select collet the same size as cutter shank.
- Clean bore, or arbor and bore, and outside of collet. Position collet in arbor.
- Screw nut on arbor until light contact is felt of nut on face of collet (see A below).

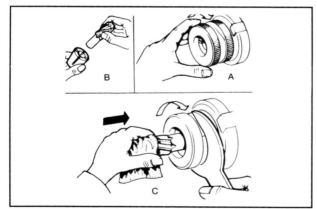

Engage cutter in arbor as follows:
- Insert cutter shank into collet (see B above).
- Slide shank into collet until end of shank is felt at rear of arbor.
- Hold cutter in position and tighten nut as tight as possible using special spanner (see C above).

Engaging arbor mounted cutters - vertical machine

Engaging a face mill on arbor

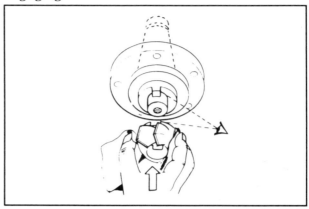

Engage arbor in machine spindle.
To engage cutter on arbor:
- Unscrew locking screw from arbor.
- Clean mating parts of cutter and arbor.
- Slide bore of cutter on arbor spigot, rotating cutter to align drive dogs to cutter slots.
- Feel drive dogs engage in slots and faces flat together.

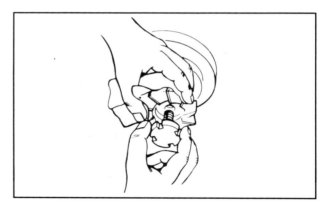

! *SAFETY — Use wiper to protect hands from sharp edges of cutter.*

Tighten cutter on arbor by holding cutter in position and screwing locking screw into arbor finger tight. Finally tighten locking screw as follows:
- Check that dogs of key and slots of screw head are not worn.
- Engage dogs of key in slots of screw head.
- Apply upward pressure to keep key engaged in slots and tighten screw.

! *SAFETY — Worn keys, or screws with worn slots, must not be used.*

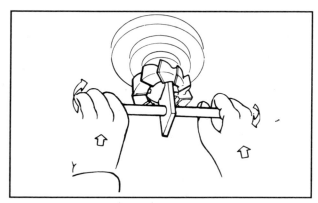

Note: Shell end mills are engaged in a similar way except:
• A socket head set screw is used as locking screw.
• The correct key must be used.
• A washer must be used between head of locking screw and shoulder of cutter.

Engaging arbor mounted cutters - horizontal machine

Engaging cutter on long arbor

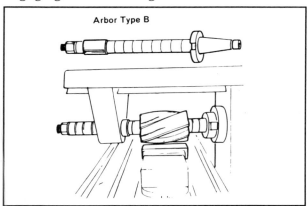

Use arbor type B when the top surface of the workpiece will pass between the arbor flange and the steady.

! *SAFETY − When using arbor type B keep clothing clear of unguarded arbor nut.*

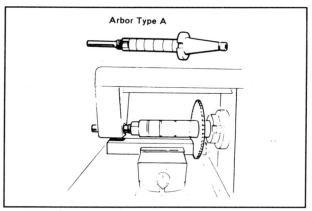

Arbors of type A are used to enable the top face of a long workpiece to be raised to just below the diameter of the spacing collars without fouling on the steady. If arbor B was used in this instance exceptionally large diameter cutters would be required. The arbor nut may be either left or right hand thread. If possible select an arbor, the nut of which tightens in the opposite direction to the required cutter rotation.

Engaging a single cutter on long arbor type B

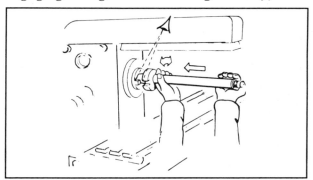

Engage arbor in machine spindle as follows:
• Set machine in low gear.
• Clean taper bore of spindle and taper shank of arbor.
• Hold arbor approximately parallel to table surface.
• Engage arbor in machine spindle, rotating arbor to align drive dogs to arbor slots.

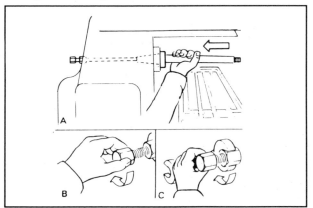

To tighten arbor in machine spindle:
• Hold arbor shank in position in spindle.
• Screw drawbar well into arbor.
• Tighten drawbar locking nut with spanner.

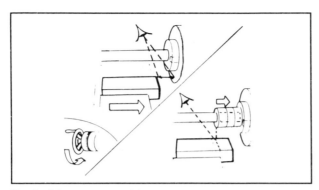

To decide cutter position:
- Hand wind the machine table in, to position the workpiece close to rear of the machine.
- Visually check that the workpiece or workholding device will clear the front of the arbor flange.
- Clean faces of collars and slide them on arbor pushing collars up to arbor flange.
- Visually check build up of collars to see outer face is level with, or protruding beyond, face to be machined.

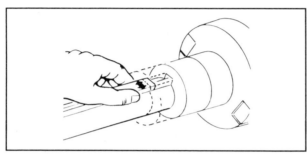

To fit key in arbor:
- Remove outer collar from arbor.
- Fit key into arbor keyway, feeling close sliding fit of key.
- Visually check that key will protrude into collar at each side of cutter.
- Replace collar on arbor rotating it to align keyway to key.

Note: When mounting thin saws on arbor:
- Omit fitting key in arbor. This allows the saw to slip if it gets trapped in workpiece.
- Trap saw between two collars when sliding onto arbor. This stops saw tilting and makes it easier to slide onto arbor.

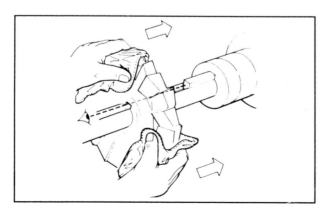

Engage cutter on arbor as follows:
- Visually check cutter is facing in direction of spindle rotation and slide cutter onto arbor.

- Rotate cutter, to align keyway to key, and push up to collars.

! *SAFETY – Protect hands from sharp edges of cutter.*

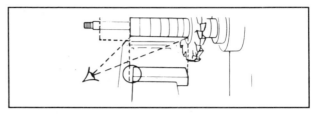

To position arbor bearing collar:
- Check position of cutter to the face to be machined.
- Adjust table setting if necessary to correct positioning.

Note: If more than one part of the workpiece is to be machined, wind the table out to position the cutter to that part of the workpiece to be machined which is closest to spindle nose.
- Slide further collars onto arbor, rotating as necessary to align keyway to key.
- Visually check build up of collars, until outer face protrudes beyond front extreme of workpiece.

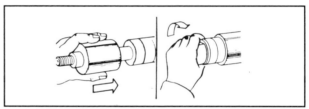

- Slide steady bearing collar up to collars on arbor.

Note: The closer the steady bearing collar is positioned to the cutter the greater the rigidity obtained when steady is positioned.
- Slide further collars onto arbor until they just protrude onto threaded part of arbor.

Note: One or more of these collars should be keyed to the arbor if the cutter has not been keyed. This ensures that the nut will not tighten if the cutter should slip.
- Visually check that sufficient thread protrudes for nut to be fully engaged. Engage nut and finger tighten.

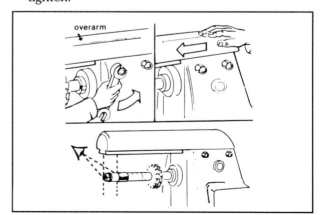

To engage overarm steady:
- Loosen overarm securing nuts.
- Slide overarm out visually checking that end protrudes beyond outer end of bearing bush.

- Wipe mating parts of overarm and steady.
- Visually align mating parts of steady and overarm.

- Engage steady on overarm, sliding to position in which the front of steady is level with end of overarm.
- Tighten nut to secure steady on overarm.
- Slide overarm in, to position steady approximately central to length of bearing bush.
- Tighten overarm securing nuts tightly.

Finally tighten cutter on arbor.
Position spanner on nut with handle approximately vertical and tighten nut securely.

! *SAFETY − Do not use worn spanner or nut.*

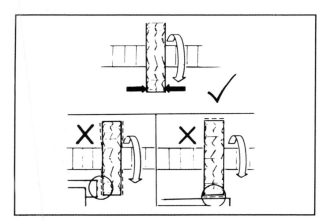

Check true running of cutter as follows:
- Check that cutter is clear of workpiece.
- Start machine spindle to run cutter at moderate speed.
- Align vision to side of cutter and fixed part of machine or workpiece to see if cutter wobbles.
- Align vision to periphery of cutter and a fixed part of machine or workpiece to check concentricity.

Note: If the cutter wobbles:
- Check that the faces of the spacing collars, cutter, arbor and securing nut are clean and undamaged.
- Check that the arbor is correctly mounted and the tapers are clean and undamaged.
- Check that the faces of the spacing collars are parallel.

If the wobble is still present:
- The arbor may be bent. Check concentricity of arbor.
- The cutter may be incorrectly ground.

Engaging cutters on long arbor type A

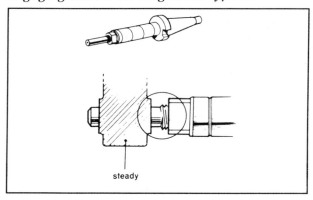

Cutters are engaged on this type of arbor in exactly the same way as on arbor type B except:
- No bearing bush is required. The pilot diameter runs in a bearing which is built into the steady.
- Visually check that the nut does not protrude on to the pilot diameter of the arbor.
- Visually check that the bearing in the steady is clear of the arbor thread.
- Visually check that the bearing in the steady does not protrude beyond end of pilot diameter.
- Key one or more of the collars between the cutter and the securing nut, if the cutter is not keyed to the arbor.

Cutting speeds, feeds and coolants (M3 – M4)

Cutting speed

The cutting speed for a metal removal operation is the speed at which the cutting edge or tooth passes over the workpiece and is usually expressed in:

- metres per minute (m/min) metric
- feet per minute (ft/min) imperial

Conversion of cutting speed to revolutions of milling cutter

- Metric:

Revolutions of milling cutter (RPM) = $\dfrac{1000\ S}{\pi\ D}$

where S = cutting speed (m/min.)
D = diameter of cutter (mm)

- Imperial:

Revolutions of milling cutter (RPM) =
$\dfrac{12 \times \text{cutting speed in feet per minute}}{\text{circumference of cutter in inches}}$

Note: The speed at which material is removed depends upon the following factors:

- The material being worked. (Hard and tough materials require a lower speed than soft and ductile materials).
- Rigidity and condition of the machine and cutting tool.
- Tool material. (Higher cutting speeds can be used for tungsten carbide tipped tools than those employed for high speed steel tools.)

Cutter feed

Cutter feed is generally expressed in:

- Millimetres per minute (mm/min) metric
- Inches per minute (ins/min) imperial

Factors influencing feed are:

- Tooth pitch
- Rigidity of workpiece and set-up
- Machine condition
- Quality of finish required
- Cutter diameter
- Type of material being worked
- Width and depth of cut.

Spindle speed

The spindle speed is expressed in revolutions per minute (RPM).

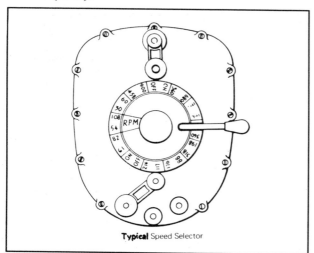

Typical Speed Selector

Selecting spindle speeds

The range of spindle speeds available from the machine gearbox is usually shown on a circular scale which is rotated until the required speed is in line with a pointer. The position of this control varies according to machine type and may be mounted on the knee or on the column.

Feed

Selecting feed rate

This is the rate at which the workpiece advances into the cutter.

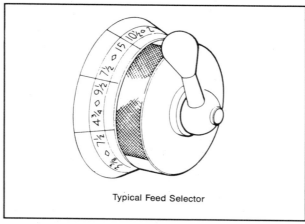

Typical Feed Selector

Feed is usually selected on the machine gearbox by rotating a dial or circular scale until the required feed is in line with a pointer.

As with the speed selector, the position of this control varies with machine type.

Cutting fluids

These are used to:

- Cool the workpiece and tool.
- Lubricate the tool face and reduce friction.
- Prevent adhesion of metal chips to the cutting tool.
- Wash away chips and swarf.

Coolants possess a high capacity to remove heat and thus have high wetting properties to ensure maximum heat transfer.

There are two main types of cutting fluid:

- Soluble oils.
- Neat oils.

Soluble oils are further sub-divided into two types:

- Opaque – most general purpose soluble oils are this type, giving a milky emulsion when diluted with water.
- Clear – used mainly for grinding operations.
- Neat oils are undiluted and are used where more severe conditions of metal removal are encountered.

The selection of the correct cutting fluid is influenced by:

- The nature of the material being machined.
- The nature of the operation being performed.
- Tool type.
- Rate of metal removal.

A sample list of coolants and their application is shown below:

Material	Cutting fluid
Mild steel	Soluble oil, mineral lard oil
Tool steel (carbon high speed)	Soluble oil, lard oil with sulphur
Alloy steel	Soluble oil, mineral lard oil
Brass and bronze	Dry, lard oil
Aluminium	Kerosene, lard oil
Malleable iron	Soluble oil
Cast iron	Dry

Workholding (M5 – M6)

Setting vice parallel with tenons

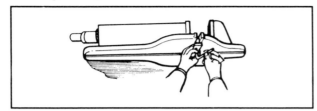

Tilt vice on to side on floor and insert tenons into tenon slots as follows:
- Check tenons are clean and free from burrs.
- Clean tenon slots.
- Insert tenons in slots, and ensure cap screw holes in tenons are in line with tapped holes in vice.
- Insert cap head screws and tighten.

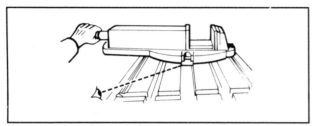

To position and clamp vice to table:
- Lower vice to machine table with tenons approximately central to table slots.
- Engage tenons in table slots.
- Check vice to ensure a good seating on table, without movement.
- Tighten securing bolts.

Setting vice parallel without tenons

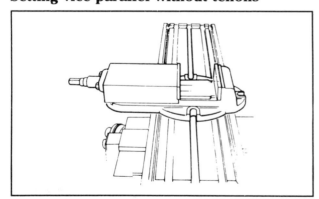

To position vice approximately parallel:
- Check that vice is clean and free of burrs.
- Position vice so as to obtain maximum support from machine table.
- Align vice slots approximately central to table slot.

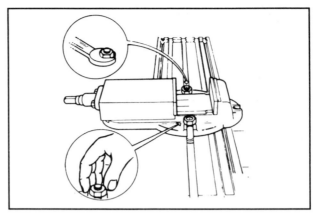

To lightly clamp vice to table:
- Ensure the clearance between bolts and vice slots is sufficient to allow for movement.
- Form fulcrum by tightening one securing bolt.

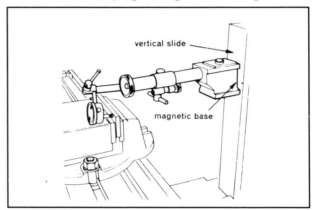

To position dial indicator:
- Ensure that the magnetic base is firmly attached to vertical slide.
- Engage dial indicator stylus on fulcrum end of fixed vice jaw or on to a parallel held in vice.
- Keep dial indicator body and stand clear of vice.

Check vice alignment as follows:
- Wind table longitudinally to pass dial indicator to opposite end of jaw, visually checking dial indicator pointer movement.

Note: Use the dial indicator readings near the extremes of the jaw to obtain greatest accuracy.
- Tap the side of the vice body at the handle end of the vice to correct any error.

Note: Always tap the vice to move the workpiece away from the stylus.

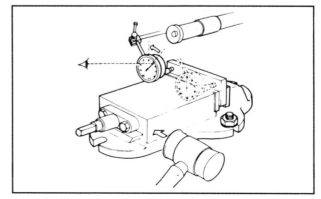

Finally, clamp the vice as follows:
- Take care when clamping to avoid movement of vice.

- Check alignment after clamping.
- Adjust setting if any movement has occurred.

Note: The same method is employed to set the vice square across the table.

Clamping regular shaped workpiece in vice

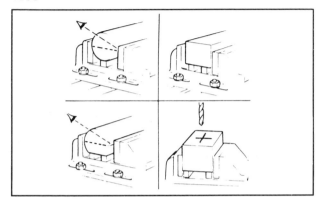

To position workpiece in vice:

- Position maximum possible length and depth of workpiece in vice, ensuring cutters will not foul vice.
- If it is necessary to raise height of workpiece, position one parallel central if bottom of workpiece is round, or one parallel to each edge if bottom of workpiece is flat.
- Check that parallel will not foul cutters or measuring instruments.
- Visually check centre line of round workpiece is below top of vice jaw.

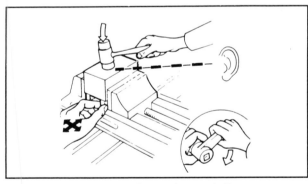

Seat workpiece and tighten vice as follows:

- Lightly tighten vice and tap workpiece down with soft hammer. A ringing sound is heard until workpiece is seated, when a dull thudding sound is heard.
- Check workpiece is correctly seated to vice bed with feeler gauge. If parallels are used ensure that they are tightly trapped.
- Tighten vice.

Setting to datum face

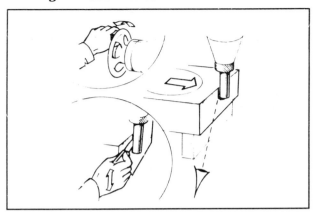

Set workpiece and clamp in position ensuring accurate alignment of face which is to be used as datum.

Set to face as follows:

- Engage setting bar in machine spindle and check concentricity.
- Position setting bar approximately central to face and approximately 0.25mm (.010″) from it.
- Position feeler gauge between setting bar and face.
- Slide feeler gauge up and down and wind table towards bar until feeler gauge is lightly trapped but can still be moved up and down.

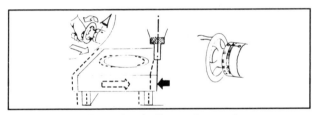

To set centre line of spindle to datum face:

- Lower table to allow bottom of setting bar to clear workpiece.
- Handwind table, half the diameter of setting bar plus thickness of feeler gauge used, to bring centre line of setting bar directly over datum face.
- 'Zero' index.

The table may now be traversed to the required position.

Note: If setting is required in two planes the same procedure is adopted.

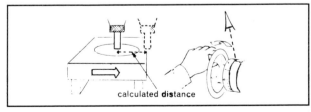

calculated distance

Index to position spindle by calculating the amount of movement required, and moving table to the required position.

Index up to a face to be machined as follows:

- Set cutter in machine spindle and measure its diameter.
- Add half the diameter of cutter to given dimension if face/s are on opposite side of workpiece to datum.

- Subtract half the diameter of cutter from given dimension if face/s are on the same side of workpiece as datum.
- Calculate amount of table movement required, and move the table the calculated amount.
- Accommodate backlash where necessary.

Setting work to marking out

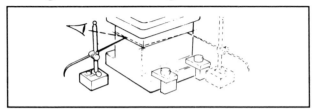

Position workpiece as follows:
- Visually judge marked out lines approximately aligned in required plane/s.
- Lightly clamp workpiece in position.

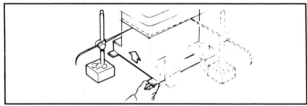

To set to horizontal marked out line/s:
- Hold base of surface gauge flat on table and adjust point of scriber to setting line, or to lines marked at equal height round workpiece.
- Check at each extreme of workpiece to see amount of error.
- Adjust workpiece with packing strips, until marked out line is aligned to point of scriber.

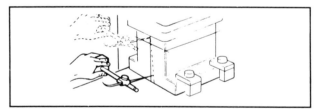

Set to vertical marked out line/s as follows:
- Hold base of surface gauge flat on vertical slide and adjust point of scriber to a line marked vertically on workpiece.
- Check line at top and bottom of workpiece to see amount of error.

- Adjust workpiece with packing strips until marked out line is aligned to point of scriber.
- Check line on the same setting at the opposite end of workpiece.
- Adjust workpiece until the line is aligned to scriber point.
- Repeat checking and adjusting until the line at each end of workpiece is correctly aligned.

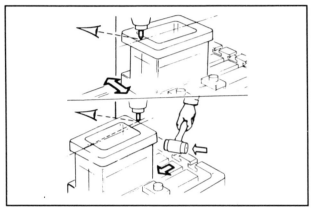

Set to longitudinal or traverse marked out lines as follows:
- Engage centre in machine spindle.
- Position centre to marked out line at one end of workpiece.
- Move table and check position of line at opposite end of workpiece.
- Tap workpiece round until line is aligned to point of scriber.
- Repeat checking and adjusting until the marked out line is aligned to the centre at each end of workpiece.

Milling operations (M7 – M11)

Milling a block square

Set workpiece in vice as follows:
- Select a pair of parallels of sufficient height to allow workpiece to be finished without cutter fouling vice jaws, but to hold maximum amount of block.
- De-burr block and clean vice jaws.
- Place smoothest side of block to fixed vice jaw.
- Rest block on parallels, approximately central to length of vice.

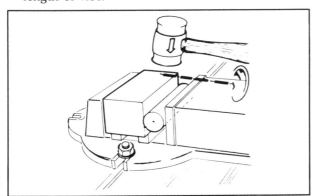

- Insert a round bar of suitable length, and approximately 20 mm diameter, between movable jaw and block, and approximately central to length of block in vice.
- Tighten vice and tap workpiece, to bring in same plane as parallels.
- Fully tighten vice and tap again.

Note: Block may not seat tight on parallels in its rough state.

To machine first face:
- Place a parallel on top of vice body to direct coolant back to table.
- Remove enough material to give a good clean face using plenty of coolant.
- Clear swarf from vice.
- Check surface finish.

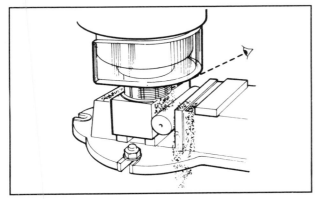

Reset block in vice as follows:
- Remove block from vice.
- Clean vice and parallels, and remove burrs from block.
- Place machined side of block to fixed vice jaw, insert round bar and tighten as before.
- Check machined side of block with 0.04 mm feeler gauge, to ensure it is square to fixed vice jaw.

! *SAFETY – Handle workpiece with care to avoid sharp edges and burrs.*

Machine second face.

Check block as follows:
- Clear swarf and remove block from vice.
- De-burr block and wipe machined faces clean.
- Check the two machined faces with a square.

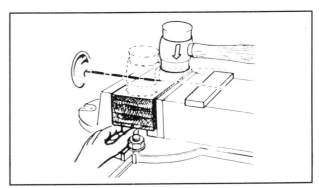

Machine third face as follows:
- Replace block in vice, one machined face to fixed vice jaw, other machined face on parallels.
- Insert bar and fully tighten vice.
- Tap block until it seats tightly on both parallels.
- Remove material to bring block to size.

To machine fourth face:
- Clean swarf, remove block and de-burr.
- Clean vice and parallels.
- Replace block with remaining unmachined side to cutter.
- Tighten vice and seat block tight on parallels.
- Machine to finished size.

Note: Bar is not used when machining the last side. When machining material such as phosphor bronze, the block should be rough machined on all four sides, leaving approximately 0.5mm all round for finishing.

General note: Although the illustrations show machining on a vertical milling machine, the same method is employed on a horizontal milling machine.

Facing to length on a vertical machine

Select cutter by selecting an end mill of sufficient length to cover face of workpiece.

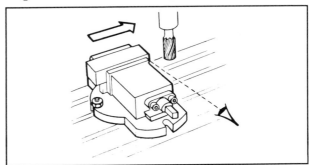

To mount workpiece:
- Select a suitable pair of parallels, and mount workpiece with top face approximately 1.5 mm ($^1/_{16}$ in) above vice jaws.
- Ensure workpiece protrudes from end of vice sufficiently to remove material required, without fouling vice jaws.
- Mount so that direction of cut is towards fixed vice jaw.

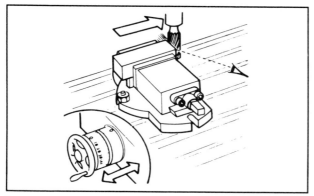

Position cutter to workpiece as follows:
- Raise table to bring end of cutter below bottom face of workpiece.
- Adjust longitudinal slide, to touch cutter lightly to workpiece, (cutter revolving).
- Set longitudinal slide at 'zero', and wind cross slide to clear cutter from workpiece.

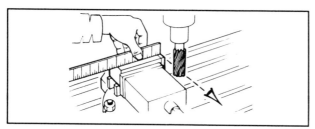

Face one end as follows:
- Check length of workpiece with rule, and note amount of material to be removed to bring to finished size.

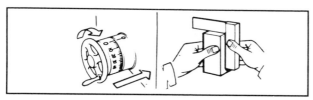

- Wind longitudinal slide required amount to remove approximately half the excess material, and lock slide.
- Power feed cross slide, using plenty of coolant.
- Check face with square.

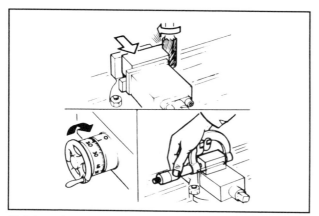

Finish to length as follows:
- Remove workpiece from vice, de-burr, clean vice jaws and parallels.

- Turn workpiece, and mount as before, ensuring cutter will not foul vice jaws at finished length.
- Touch cutter to workpiece, and remove material to bring to finished length plus approximately 0.5 mm (.020″).
- Check with micrometer, and remove material to bring to finished length.
- Re-check before removing workpiece from vice.

Machining with workpiece vertically in vice

Workpieces of short length, may be mounted vertically in the vice, being set with a square for the first face. It should be noted however, that only workpieces which will not protrude more than approximately 50 mm (2″) above vice jaws, before being faced to length, should be machined in this way.

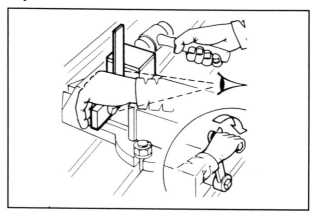

Mount workpiece as follows:
- Visually align workpiece in vertical plane, and hand tighten vice.
- Place a square on bottom face of vice, blade along vertical face of workpiece.
- Tap workpiece gently, with soft hammer, to align workpiece to square and fully tighten vice.

Select cutter by selecting a shell end mill, or face mill, of sufficient diameter to cover face of workpiece.

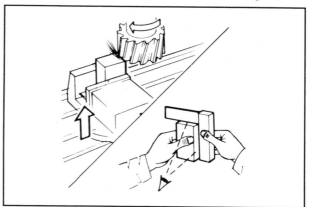

To position cutter to workpiece:
- Wind longitudinal slide, to bring cutter over workpiece.
- Raise table, cutter revolving, until cutter lightly touches workpiece.
- Raise table the minimum amount to clean up face of workpiece, and take cut.
- Check workpiece with square.

Facing to length on a horizontal machine

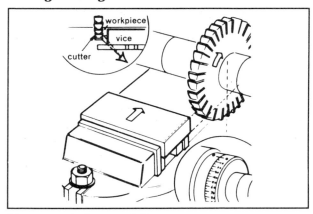

Mount workpiece as follows:
- Select a suitable pair of parallels on which to mount the workpiece.
- Ensure end of workpiece protrudes sufficiently from vice, to remove material required.
- Position workpiece so that direction of cut is towards fixed vice jaw.
- Tighten vice, and tap workpiece down until parallels are trapped.

Select cutter by selecting a side and face cutter, diameter large enough to cut full face of workpiece, without arbor collars fouling top of workpiece.

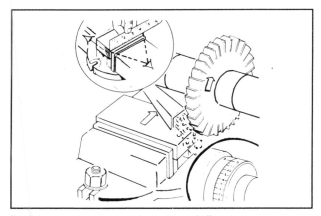

Position cutter to workpiece as follows:
- Bring face of cutter below bottom edge of workpiece and close to it.
- Start machine, lightly touch cutter to workpiece, and 'zero' index.
- Wind longitudinal slide, to clear cutter from workpiece.

Face one end of workpiece as follows:
- Check length of workpiece with rule. Note amount of material to be removed.
- Wind cross slide the required distance to remove most of the required amount, and lock slide.
- Power feed longitudinal slide, using plenty of coolant when cutting.
- Check face with square, and visually check surface texture with cutter stopped and clear of workpiece.

To face to finished size:
- Check with micrometer, and calculate finishing cut required.

- Wind cross slide the required distance and take finishing cut, using plenty of coolant.
- Check finished size and de-burr.

Note: For workpieces with excessive amounts of material on the length, two or more cuts may have to be taken to bring to finished size, and obtain a good surface texture.

Repeat technique described above for opposite end, if both ends require machining.

Facing to length with face mill

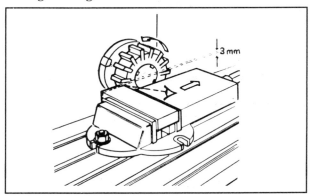

- Select cutter by selecting a face mill of slightly larger diameter than face of workpiece.
- Mount face mill on machine spindle.
- Mount workpiece.
- Position cutter to workpiece by visually setting centre of cutter approximately 3 mm below top surface of workpiece.
- Bring face of cutter close to workpiece.
- Start machine, and ensure that cut is towards fixed vice jaws and cutter will cut downwards. Lightly touch cutter to workpiece and 'zero' index.
- Face one end.
- De-burr workpiece.
- Face to finished size.

Milling a shoulder

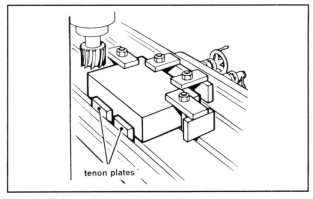

tenon plates

Mount workpiece as follows:
- Select a suitable workholding method, so that finished depth of cut can be obtained, without fouling workholding equipment or machine.
- Ensure that direction of cut is towards a fixed part of workholding, preferably to rear of machine eg, towards stops, clamps or fixed vice jaw.

Select cutter (face or end mill) of sufficient diameter to cover full face of shoulder to be machined.

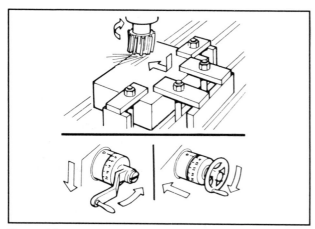

To position cutter to workpiece:
- Start machine, and lightly touch periphery of cutter, to datum face of workpiece, and 'zero' index.
- Wind table the required amount, less 0.25 mm to side face of shoulder, and lock slide.
- Lightly touch surface of workpiece with face of cutter, and 'zero' index.

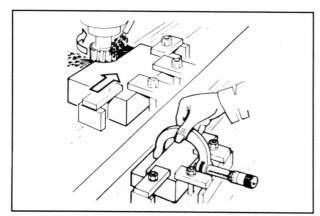

Cut out shoulder as follows:
- Adjust table to remove material in even cuts, using plenty of coolant.
- Check side of face of shoulder after a depth of approximately 3 mm has been reached.
- Check depth of shoulder , when within 0.5 mm of finished size.
- Adjust index for both side face and depth.
- Finish machine.

Note: If an end mill is employed, the full depth less 0.25 mm is first set, and the material removed by the side of the cutter.

This operation may also be performed on a horizontal milling machine, by setting up in the same manner and using an end mill or side and face cutter.

Milling tenons

Tenons are usually manufactured from rectangular bars, the four sides being first milled square to each other, and to the appropriate size. The block is then faced to length, the steps milled central to the width, and undercut if required. The corners are usually chamfered.

Mill block square.

Face to length.

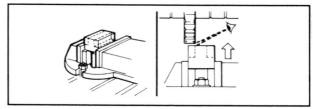

To position cutter for depth of step:
- Clean vice jaws and mount workpiece on a suitable pair of parallels, to enable full depth of step to be cut, without cutter fouling jaws.
- Raise table to bring cutter within 1 mm of top of workpiece.
- Position cross slide, to bring cutter over edge of workpiece, on fixed vice jaws.
- Ensure cutter will not cut beyond width of step.

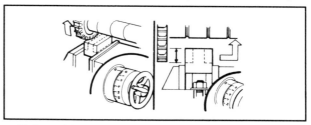

- Raise table, with cutter revolving, until workpiece is lightly marked.
- Set vertical index at 'zero'.
- Wind cross slide to clear cutter from workpiece.
- Raise the table the required amount of full depth, and reset index at 'zero'.

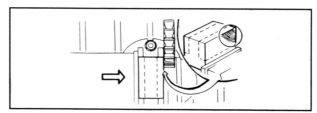

Position cutter for width of step as follows:
- Wind cross slide to position side of cutter within 1 mm of workpiece.
- Start machine and wind cross slide gently until cutter lightly marks workpiece.

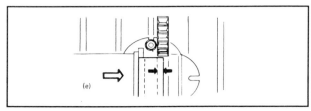

- Set index at 'zero'.
- Stop machine and wind longitudinal slide to clear cutter from workpiece.
- Wind cross slide the required amount to finish first side of step, and mark direction of movement, eg bottom dimension 25 mm, top dimension 12.5 mm finished: 6.25 mm to be removed from each side.

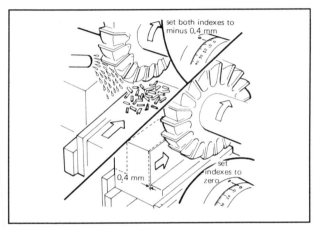

Take first cut of step as follows:
- Drop table approximately 0.4 mm from finished depth.
- Wind cross slide back approximately half a turn, and return to within 0.4 mm to 'zero', in the direction marked.
- Lock cross slide.
- Feed across workpiece, using plenty of coolant.
- Stop machine, and return table to starting point, clean swarf and coolant from workpiece.
- Check width and depth of step, to ensure index settings are correct.
- Wind both indexes to 'zero' (adjust if necessary), and finish step.

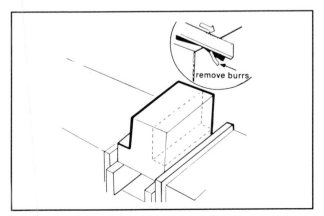

De-burr and reset workpiece as follows:
- Remove workpiece from vice, clean jaws, and parallels, and remove burrs from workpiece.
- Turn workpiece and mount opposite side to fixed vice jaw.

! SAFETY – *Handle workpiece with care to avoid sharp edges and burrs.*

To cut step:
- Repeat sequence described above.
- Remove workpiece and de-burr.
Note: When a quantity of small tenons of short length is required, a bar of up to 300 mm is milled and stepped and then cut off to the required lengths.

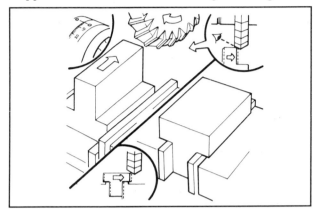

Chamfer corners as follows:
- Clean vice jaws, and insert smallest dimension in vice, steps seating on top of vice jaws.
- Mount an equal angle cutter on arbor (90° inclusive).
- Adjust cross, and vertical slides to bring cutter to workpiece, over fixed vice jaw, ensuring cutter will not foul jaws.
- Wind cross slide to touch cutter gently to workpiece, set index at 'zero'.
- Wind longitudinal slide to clear cutter from workpiece, adjust cross slide for required chamfer and take cut.
- Stop machine, clear cutter from workpiece, remove tenon from vice and de-burr.
- Turn workpiece for the opposite side chamfer.
- Mount workpiece on suitable parallels for opposite step, and ends, proceed as before.

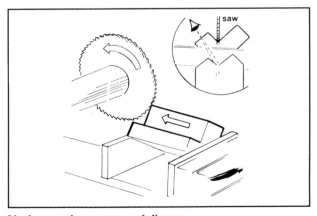

Undercut the steps as follows:
- Mount a suitable slitting saw on arbor.
- Set workpiece in vice at required angle using a protractor. Ensure saw will not foul vice jaws.
- Adjust cross slide to bring saw central to corner of step.
- With the saw revolving, raise table until saw touches workpiece.

- Visually check that saw is central to the step corner. As the saw commences to cut, two lines will appear on the workpiece. Ensure that these lines are equally spaced either side of the corner. Adjust cross slide if necessary.
- Wind longitudinal slide to clear saw from workpiece, and set vertical index at 'zero'.
- Raise table for the required depth, and take cut.

Note: The same method is used for milling tenons on vertical machines. The steps are milled with an end mill and the chamfers produced with an angular formed cutter.

❗ *SAFETY – Always wear safety glasses when using slitting saws. Keep hands well clear of saw.*

Milling a slot

Set vice parallel.

To set for position of slot with setting bar:
- Open vice jaws to give plenty of clearance for setting bar.
- Engage setting bar and position approximately central to vice.
- Check setting bar for concentricity.
- Raise table to enable setting bar to register on fixed vice jaw.
- Move table across until bar is within 1.5 mm of the fixed vice jaw.

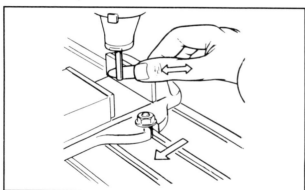

- Insert a 0.03 mm feeler gauge, and carefully wind table across to trap feeler between bar and fixed vice jaw. Rock feeler gently until tightness is obtained.
- Zero index.
- Wind table back the required distance *minus* half the diameter of the setting bar, to give the correct centre position for the slot.
- Wind table at least 0.75 mm past the required setting and then wind it back to correct setting, to take up any free movement (backlash) in the leadscrew.

Note: Position of the slot may be central to the workpiece or a specific distance from one side.

Set workpiece in vice as follows:
- Ensure workpiece is free of burrs and the vice is clean.
- Seat on a pair of parallels (if necessary) to bring top of workpiece approximately 5 mm above vice jaws. Parallels to be tight after seating.

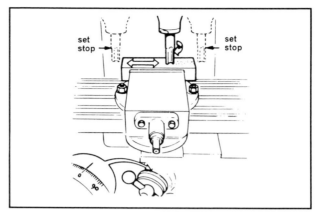

To set for depth and cutting slot:
- Engage and check concentricity of cutter.
- Touch top of workpiece (with cutter revolving), marking the workpiece very lightly.
- Set vertical index at 'zero'.
- Set traverse stops at each end of table, to stop traverse when cutter has completely cleared workpiece at each end.
- Remove material in even cuts. Take cut from each end of workpiece alternately.

❗ *SAFETY – Switch off machine*

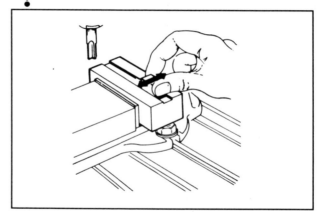

- Check width of slot with slip gauges, after a depth of 1.5 mm has been obtained.
- Check position of slot with a micrometer or vernier after a depth of 3 mm has been obtained.
- Check depth of slot with depth micrometer or vernier when within 0.025 mm of full depth on index.

❗ *SAFETY – Cutter to be well clear of workpiece and stopped and any swarf removed before checking slot.*

Note: It is possible to cut many types of slot on a vertical mill. The slot may not cover the whole workpiece, in which case an index reading must be taken or a stop set for the blind end (see Milling a keyway).

A stub arbor may be employed together with a side and face cutter. Round workpieces are usually set in the dividing head for this operation.

Alternative method

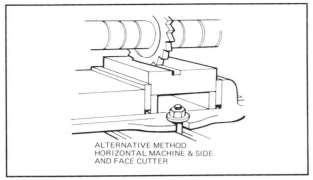

ALTERNATIVE METHOD
HORIZONTAL MACHINE & SIDE
AND FACE CUTTER

The operation may be carried out on a horizontal machine in the same manner, when a side and face or slot cutter is employed. Alternatively the workpiece may be clamped to the rear of the machine table, or to an angle bracket, and a slot drill mounted in the machine spindle.

Milling a keyway

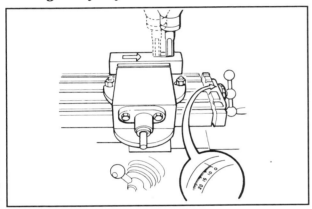

Repeat sequences as for Milling a slot.
Set cutter to length of keyway as follows:
- Engage and check concentricity of cutter.
- Touch end of workpiece with cutter and paper (as in setting cutter central).
- Wind table the required length from end of workpiece, *plus* diameter of cutter, using table index.
- Set index at 'zero'.
- Wind table to the required length of keyway *minus* diameter of cutter, and mark index.

Note: Backlash must be accounted for when moving in reverse direction.

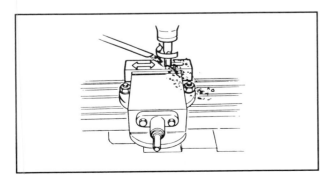

Set for depth and cut keyway as follows:

- Touch top of workpiece with revolving cutter marking the workpiece very lightly.
- Set vertical index at 'zero'.
- Remove metal in even cuts, until required depth is reached.
- Use plenty of coolant to aid swarf clearance.
- Switch off machine.

To check width and length of keyway check width of keyway with slip gauges, also check length with a rule or vernier caliper when a depth of 1.5 mm has been obtained.

Note: The operation can be carried out on a horizontal machine by selecting a workholding method to position the workpiece at the rear of machine table.

Milling vees on a horizontal machine

Vees are milled with an arbor mounted angle cutter. Alternatively, the workpiece may be marked out, and set at the required angle, in the vice.

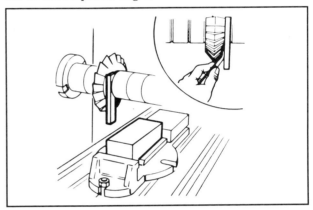

Milling vees with equal angle cutter
Mount cutter on arbor.
Prepare arbor for cutter positioning as follows:
- Loosen arbor locking nut, and insert a small parallel bar, between cutter and collar.
- Ensure parallel protrudes approximately 6 mm below diameter of cutter.
- Tighten arbor locking nut.
- Check between cutter boss and parallel, with feeler gauge, to ensure a good seat.

Note: The cutter should be checked to ensure that the angles are ground equally about the centre.

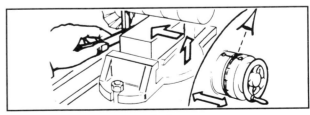

To position cutter to workpiece:
- Bring parallel close to end of workpiece.
- Insert a feeler gauge between parallel and workpiece, and gently move across slide to lightly trap it.

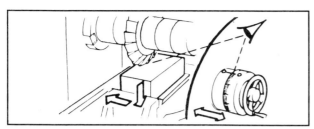

- 'Zero' the index. Drop table to clear parallel from workpiece.
- Wind cross slide the required distance to position centre of cutter. Reset index on 'zero'.

$$\text{Distance of centre of vee from end of workpiece} + \frac{\text{width of cutter}}{2} +$$

$$\text{thickness of parallel} + \text{thickness of feeler gauge} = \text{required distance}$$

- Loosen arbor locking nut, remove parallel, and re-tighten.

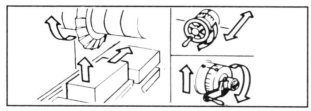

Set cutter for depth as follows:
- Bring cutter over face of workpiece.
- Raise table (cutter revolving), to bring cutter so that points of cutter lightly mark workpiece.
- 'Zero' index.

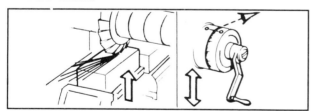

Cut the vee as follows:
- Remove material in even cuts, until about 6 mm depth has been reached.
- Use plenty of coolant, remove swarf with brush, (cutter stopped).
- Reduce depth of cut after 6 mm depth has been reached.

Milling vees with workpiece set at an angle
Vees of 90°, or more, inclusive angle may be cut using the following method. If the inclusive angle required is less than 90° an appropriate angled cutter must be employed.

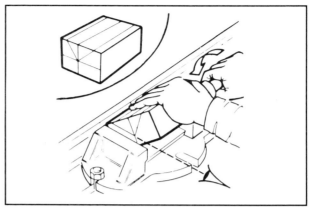

Mark out workpiece by applying marking blue to workpiece. Mark centre line and width of vee on top face, and depth of vee and correct angle on each end.
Mount workpiece as follows:
- Set workpiece in vice, visually align one marked line of vee in horizontal plane, using top of vice as a guide.
- Ensure workpiece is as low as possible in vice, with marked horizontal line slightly above vice jaw.
- Hand tighten vice to hold workpiece in position.

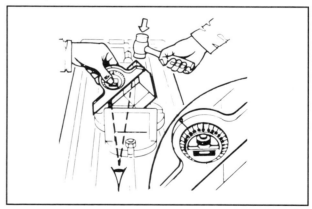

Set workpiece at required angle as shown in diagram, using protractor or clinometer.
Note: When using 'bubble' instruments first check table level and where appropriate take observed errors into account when setting workpiece.

Select cutter by selecting a side and face cutter, diameter large enough to cut the full depth of vee, without arbor collars fouling workpiece.

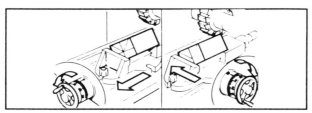

To cut the vee:
- Bring face of cutter above horizontal line of workpiece.
- Let cutter just touch workpiece. 'Zero' index.
- Wind longitudinal slide to clear cutter from workpiece, and wind on cut with cross slide.

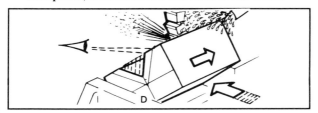

- Remove material in even cuts, until side of cutter is close to vertical marked line.

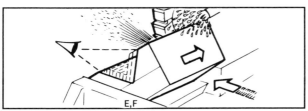

- Return table to starting point, gently raise table so that face of cutter just splits horizontal line on workpiece.
- Remove material in even cuts as before, until side of cutter splits the vertical line on workpiece.

Note: The finishing cut will aid the surface texture obtained. If the material is removed in one cut, the pressure will tend to force the face of the cutter down, and so cut below the horizontal line of the vee.

When the included angle is greater than 90°, each angle of the vee should be set and machined individually, the position of the vee first being marked out on the workpiece.

Milling an angle by setting the work at an angle

Mark out workpiece by applying marking blue to workpiece, and scribe the required angle in the appropriate position.

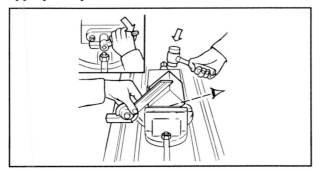

To set workpiece at required angle:
- Mount workpiece in vice, visually align scribed line with top of vice jaws.
- Set workpiece with line approximately 3 mm ($^1/_8''$) above vice jaws.
- Hand tighten vice, to hold workpiece steady.
- Set a protractor at the required angle, hold the base firmly on machine table and check face alignment.
- Tap workpiece with soft hammer, until exact alignment is obtained.
- Fully tighten vice.
- Re-check with protractor, to ensure workpiece has not moved.

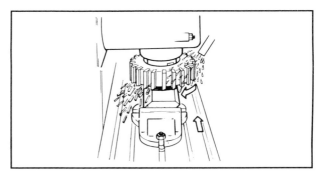

Position cutter to workpiece as follows:
- Raise table to bring bottom face of cutter within approximately 1.5mm ($^1/_{16}''$) of highest point of workpiece.
- Adjust cross slide to cover whole face of angle with cutter, and lock slide.
- Start machine, and remove material, until scribed line is split.

Note: For the first few cuts offset the workpiece to the cutter centreline to ensure that the direction of thrust in cutting is directed towards the fixed vice jaw. This tends to prevent the workpiece 'tipping' while cutting is in progress.

After the first cut the surface area will become greater, and the depth of cut should be less for subsequent cuts.